A Growing Natio

I'VE BEEN WORKIN' ON THE RAILROAD

Railroad Work Song

I've been work-in' on the rail-road, All the live-long day,

I've been work-in' on the rail-road, Just to pass the time a-

way, Don't you hear the whis-tle blow-in', Rise up so ear-ly in the

morn; Don't you hear the cap-tain shout-ing, "Di-nah, blow your

horn!" Di-nah, won't you blow, Di-nah, won't you blow,

Di-nah, won't you blow your horn,— Di-nah, won't you blow,

Di-nah, won't you blow, Di-nah, won't you blow your horn!

Some-one's in the kit-chen with Di-nah, Some-one's in the

Kit-chen, I know,——Some-one's in the kit-chen with Di-nah,

Strum-min' on the old ban-jo And sing-in', Fee, Fi,

Fid-dlee-i-o, Fee, Fi, Fid-dlee-i-o,—— Fee, Fi,

Fid-dlee-i-o, Strum-min' on the old ban-jo.

The year 1830 marked the beginning of the railroad era in the US. The Gold Rush in 1849
speeded its development and in 1869 the rails stretched from the Atlantic to the Pacific when
the Union Pacific and Central Pacific Railroads were joined at Promontory, Utah.

John Henry was a black railroad worker who apparently died around 1873 during the construction of the Big Bend Tunnel in West Virginia on the C & O railroad.

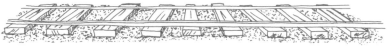

JOHN HENRY

Railroad Ballad

1. When John Hen-ry was a lit-tle ba-by,— Sit-tin' on his dad-dy's knee, He picked up a ham-mer and a lit-tle piece of steel, said, "This ham-mer's gon-na be the death of me, Lawd, Lawd, This ham-mer's gon-na be the death of me."

2. Well, the Captain said to John Henry,
   "Gonna bring that steam drill 'round.
   Gonna bring that steam drill out on the job,
   Gonna whop that steel on down, Lawd, Lawd,
   Gonna whop that steel on down."
3. John Henry told his captain,
   Said, "A man ain't nothin' but a man,
   But before I'd let that steam drill beat me down,
   I'd die with this hammer in my hand, Lawd, Lawd,
   I'd die with this hammer in my hand."

4. Well, the man that invented the steam drill,
      He thought he was mighty fine,
   But John Henry drove his fifteen feet,
      And the steam drill only made nine, Lawd, Lawd,
   The stream drill only made nine.

5. John Henry was hammerin' on the mountain,
      And his hammer was strikin' fire,
   He drove so hard that he broke his poor old heart,
      And he laid down his hammer and he died, Lawd, Lawd,
   He laid down his hammer and he died.

6. They took John Henry to the graveyard,
      And they buried him in the sand,
   And ev'ry locomotive that comes roarin' by
      Says, "There lies a steel drivin' man," Lawd, Lawd,
   here lies a steel drivin' man."

7

The Irishmen who worked on the railroads were called "tarriers." Two explanations for this name have been passed down: One, that their red, stubby beards made them look like terrier dogs; or two, that they did not tarry (move slowly) as they worked.

DRILL, YE TARRIERS

T.C.   *Thomas Casey, 1888*

1. Ev-'ry morn-ing at sev-en o'clock, There's twen-ty tar-ri-ers a-work-in' on the rock, And the boss comes a-long and he says, "Keep still, And come down heav-y on the cast i-ron drill."

*Optional chords for guitar: Key of Am (Am, E⁷, G)

And drill, ye tar-ri-ers, drill. Drill, ye tar-ri-ers,

drill. For it's work all day for su-gar in your tay,

Down be-yond the rail-way, And drill, ye

tar-ri-ers, drill! And blast! And fire!—

2. Our new foreman was Dan McCann,
   By gosh, he was a blame mean man;
  Last week a premature blast went off,
   And a mile in the air went big Jim Goff.
     Chorus
3. Next time pay day comes around,
   Jim Goff a dollar short was found;
  "What for?" says he, then this reply,
   "You're docked for the time you were up in the sky."
     Chorus

During the Irish potato famine of 1840, thousands of Irishmen came to America. Many found jobs working on the railroads.

PADDY WORKS ON THE RAILWAY

Railroad Ballad

1. In eight-een hun-dred and for-ty one, I put me cor-du-roy breech-es on, I put me cor-du-roy breech-es on To work up-on the rail-way.

Chorus:
Fil-i-me-oo-ree-eye-ree-ay, Fil-i-me-oo-ree-eye-ree-ay, Fil-i-me-oo-ree-eye-ree-ay, To work up-on the rail-way.

2. It's "Pat, do this" and "Pat, do that," without a stocking or cravat*,
   And nothing but an old straw hat, while Pat works on the railway.
   Chorus
3. And, when Pat lays him down to sleep, the wiry bugs around him creep,
   And hardly a bit can poor Pat sleep, while he works on the railway.
   Chorus

* necktie or scarf

10

After the Civil War, cattle raising became an important industry. Cowboys trailed herds to railroad towns where dealers shipped the cattle to Chicago and other meat-packing centers. The Chisholm Trail, which ran from the Mexican border through Texas to Abilene, Kansas, was often used.

THE OLD CHISHOLM TRAIL

Cowboy Song

1. Oh, come a-long boys and lis-ten to my tale, I'll—
tell you of my trou-bles on the old Chis-holm Trail,

(Chorus)
Sing-in' Ki-yi yip-pi yip-pi yay, yip-pi

yay! Sing-in' Ki-yi yip-pi yip-pi yay.——

2. I started on the trail on June twenty-third,
    With a drove of Texas cattle, 2000 in the herd,
        Chorus

3. I'm up in the mornin' before daylight,
    And before I sleep, the moon shines bright,
        Chorus

4. Oh, it's bacon and beans 'most every day,
    I'd as soon be a-eatin' prairie hay,
        Chorus

5. My feet are in the stirrups and my rope is on the side,
    Show me a hoss that I can't ride,
        Chorus

* Optional chords for guitar: Key of E (E, B⁷)

11

GOOD-BYE, OLD PAINT

Cowboy Song

1. My foot in the stir-rup, my po-ny won't stand,—
I'm a-leav-in' Chey-enne, I'm off for Mon-tan';—

Chorus
Good-bye, old Paint, I'm a-leav-in' Chey-enne,
Good-bye, old Paint, I'm a-leav-in' Chey-enne.

2. I'm a-ridin' old Paint, I'm a-leadin' old Dam,
  Good-bye, little Annie, I'm off for Montan'.
      Chorus
3. Oh, hitch up your horses and feed 'em some hay,
  And seat yourself by me as long as you stay.
      Chorus
4. My horses ain't hungry, they'll not eat your hay,
  My wagon is loaded and rolling away.
      Chorus

Optional accomp: Play only D chord throughout.

12

I RIDE AN OLD PAINT

Cowboy Song

I ride an old paint,*—I lead an old dam,*—I'm goin' to Mon-tan-a to throw the hoo-li-han.* They feed in the cou-lees,* they wa-ter in the draw,* Their tails are all mat-ted, their backs are all raw.

Chorus

Ride a-round, lit-tle do-gies,* Ride a-round—them—slow, For the fi-'ry*and snuf-fy*are rar-in' to go.

* Definitions:
paint - spotted horse
dam - mother of a foal
throw the hoolihan - to rope a steer and wrestle to the ground
coulees - ravines
draw - a ravine which drains water after a hard rain
dogies - motherless calves
fiery - spirited
snuffy - disagreeable

Cattle that weren't driven to railroad towns were often trailed to stock ranges in northern states such as Wyoming, Montana and the Dakotas. These ranges were left open to grazing when buffalo herds were destroyed.

GIT ALONG, LITTLE DOGIES*

Cowboy Song, 1860's

1. As I was a-walk-ing one morn-ing for pleas-ure, I spied a cow punch-er a-rid-ing a-long. His hat was throwed back and his spurs was a-jing-ling, And as he ap-proached, he was sing-ing this song:

* motherless calves

14

Whoop-ee ti - yi -yo, git a-long lit-tle do-gies, It's your mis-for-tune and none of my own. Whoop-ee ti-yi-yo, git a-long lit-tle do-gies, For you know Wy-o-ming will be your new home.

2. It's early in spring that we round up the dogies,
    We mark 'em and brand 'em and bob off their tails,
  We round up the horses, load up the chuck wagon,
    And then throw the dogies out on the long trail.
        Chorus
3. Some fellows go up the trail for pleasure,
    But that's where they get it most awfully wrong,
  For you haven't an idea the trouble they give us,
    As we go driving those dogies along.
        Chorus

15

MY HOME'S IN MONTANA

Cowboy Song

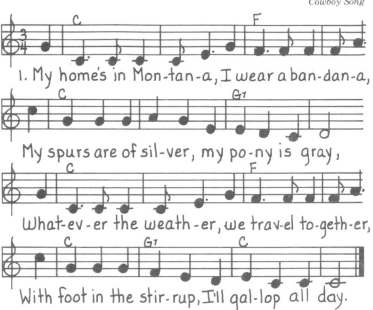

1. My home's in Mon-tan-a, I wear a ban-dan-a,

My spurs are of sil-ver, my po-ny is gray,

What-ev-er the weath-er, we trav-el to-geth-er,

With foot in the stir-rup, I'll gal-lop all day.

2. We're up with the sun, there's work to be done,
   In the wide open spaces, that's where we would be,
   Out here in the West is the life we love best,
   Montana is home for my pony and me.

3. When far from the ranches, I chop the pine branches
   To heap on the campfire as daylight grows pale,
   When I have partaken of beans and of bacon,
   I whistle a cheery old song of the trail.

16

The lives of the roving cowboys changed when the government opened the land to farmers and ranchers who staked out their homesteads and fenced their property.

OLD TEXAS

Cowboy Song

1. I'm goin' to leave (I'm goin' to leave) ol'—Tex-as

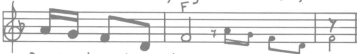

now, (ol'—Tex-as now,) They've got no use (They've got no use)

for the long-horned cow. (for the long-horned cow.)

clip, clop, clip, clop,

2. They've plowed and fenced my cattle range,
   And the people there are all so strange.
3. I'll take my horse, I'll take my rope,
   And hit the trail upon a lope*.
4. I'll bid adios to the Alamo,
   And set my face toward Mexico.
5. I'll spend my days on the wide, wide range,
   For the people there are not so strange.
6. The hard, hard ground will be my bed,
   And the saddle seat will hold my head.
7. And when I waken from my dreams,
   I'll eat my bread and my sardines.

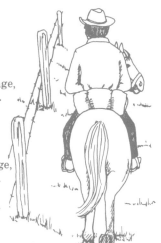

* gallop

In the 1890s, a tiny black bug from Mexico called a boll weevil invaded the Texas cotton fields by the millions. Nothing could stop them and they multiplied quickly. Great destruction of crops occurred and poverty followed.

THE BOLL WEEVIL

Southern Ballad

1. The boll wee-vil is a —— lit-tle black bug, Come from Mex-i-co they say, Come all the way to —— Tex-as, Just a-look-in' for a place to stay, Just a-look-in' for a home, (Just a-look-in' for a home, Just a-look-in' for a home. (Just a-look-in' for a home.)

2. The first time I saw the boll weevil,
    He was sittin' on the square;
  The next time I saw the boll weevil,
    He had all of his family there,
  Just a-lookin' for a home, (Just a-lookin' for a home,)
    Just a-lookin' for a home. (Just a-lookin' for a home.)
3. The farmer took the boll weevil
    And buried him in hot sand;
  The boll weevil said to the farmer,
    "I'll stand it like a man,
  For it is my home, (For it is my home,)
    For it is my home." (For it is my home.")
4. The farmer took the boll weevil,
    And put him in a lump of ice;
  The boll weevil said to the farmer,
    "This is mighty cool and nice,
  It'll be my home, (It'll be my home,)
    It'll be my home." (It'll be my home.")
5. The boll weevil said to the farmer,
    "You better leave me alone;
  I ate up all your cotton,
    Now I'm gonna start on your corn,
  I'll have a home, (I'll have a home,)
    I'll have a home." (I'll have a home.")

PICK A BALE O' COTTON

Southern Work Song

1. Gon-na jump down, turn a-round,
pick a bale o' cot-ton, Gon-na jump down,
turn a-round, pick a bale a day.

(Chorus)
Oh, Law-dy, pick a bale o' cot-ton,
Oh, Law-dy, pick a bale a day.

2. Me and my partner can pick a bale o' cotton,
   Me and my partner can pick a bale a day.
      Chorus
3. I b'lieve to my soul I can pick a bale o' cotton,
   I b'lieve to my soul I can pick a bale a day.
      Chorus
4. Gonna pick a, pick a, pick a, pick a, pick a bale o'cotton,
   Gonna pick a, pick a, pick a, pick a, pick a bale a day.
      Chorus

*Optional chords for guitar: Key of E (E, A, B⁷)

Although impossible to hand-pick a bale (500 lbs.) of cotton in one day, this rhythmic work song livened up the workers as they bent between the thorny rows of cotton plants.

20

COTTON NEEDS PICKIN'

Southern Work Song

Cot-ton needs a-pick-in' so bad, Cot-ton needs a-pick-in' so bad,— Cot-ton needs a-pick-in' so bad, I'm gon-na pick all o-ver this field.

Suggestion: One group can sing "Cotton Needs Pickin' " while another group sings (at the same time) "Pick a Bale o' Cotton."

SHUCKIN' OF THE CORN

Midwest Folk Song

I'm a-go-in' to the shuck-in' of the corn,— I'm a-go-in' to the shuck-in' of the corn,— A-shuck-in' of the corn and a-blow-in' of the horn, I'm a-go-in' to the shuck-in' of the corn.—

The Gold Rush kept prospectors following new leads across the West, but most of the searches ended in dismal failure. However, those that gave up mining often settled in the West and new communities were formed.

OLD SETTLER'S SONG

Northwest Ballad

1. I've wan-dered all o-ver this coun-try,— Pros-pect-ing and dig-ging for gold, I've tun-neled, hy-drau-licked and cra-dled, And I have been fre-quent-ly sold. And I have been fre-quent-ly sold,— And I have been fre-quent-ly sold. I've tun-neled, hy-drau-licked and cra-dled, And I have been fre-quent-ly sold.

22

2. For each man who got rich by mining,
   Perceiving that hundreds grew poor,
   I made up my mind to try farming,
   The only pursuit that was sure.

   Chorus: The only pursuit that was sure,
   The only pursuit that was sure,
   I made up my mind to try farming,
   The only pursuit that was sure.*

3. So, rolling my grub in my blanket,
   I left all my tools on the ground,
   I started one morning to shank it
   For the country they call Puget Sound.
   Chorus

4. When I looked on the prospects so gloomy,
   The tears trickled over my face,
   And I thought that my troubles had brought me,
   To the end of the jumping-off place.
   Chorus

5. I tried to get out of the country,
   But poverty forced me to stay,
   Until I became an old settler,
   Then nothing could drive me away.
   Chorus

6. No longer the slave of ambition,
   I laugh at the world and its shams,
   As I think of my pleasant condition
   Surrounded by acres of clams.
   Chorus

* The choruses of the remaining verses are similarly formed by repetition of the fourth and third lines.

During the California Gold Rush of 1849, many songs were created by putting new words to familiar tunes. This melody is Stephen Foster's "Camptown Races."

SACRAMENTO

Sea Chantey*, 1850

1. A bul-ly ship and a bul-ly crew, With a hoo-da and a hoo-da, A bul-ly mate and a cap-tain, too, Hoo-da, hoo-da ay.

(Chorus) Then blow ye winds, hi-oh, For Cal-i-for-ny-o, There's plen-ty of gold, so I've been told, On the banks of the Sac-ra-men-to.

2. Around Cape Horn in the month of snow,
   With a hoo-da, and a hoo-da,
  We came to the land where the riches flow,
   Hoo-da, hoo-da ay.
       Chorus

Suggestion: One person sings solo on first phrases, group joins in on "hoo-da's" and chorus.

* A chantey (shan' ti) is a song that sailors sing in rhythm with motions while working.

24

BLOW YE WINDS

Sea Chantey

1. 'Tis ad-ver-tised in Bos-ton town, New York and Buf-fa-lo,
Five hun-dred brave A-mer-i-cans, A-whal-ing for to go,—

Chorus
sing-ing, Blow ye winds of morn-ing; Blow ye winds, heigh-ho!
Haul a-way your run-ning gear And blow, ye winds, heigh-ho!

2. They send you to New Bedford fair,
   That famous whaling port,
   And give you to some strangers there
   To board and fit you out, singing,
   Chorus
3. They tell you of the clipper ships,
   A-running in and out,
   And say you'll take five hundred whale
   Before you're six months out, singing,
   Chorus
4. And now we're out to sea, my boys,
   The wind comes on to blow,
   One half the watch is sick on deck,
   The other half below, singing,
   Chorus

*Optional chords for guitar: Key of E (E, B⁷, A, F#⁷)

During the 1760's, colonists in New Bedford, Massachusetts began a whaling industry. The greatest period of American whaling was from 1830-60. When a whaling ship left port, the crew could expect a two-year voyage filled with thrills and danger.

CAPE COD CHANTEY

Sea Chantey

1. Cape Cod girls, they have no combs, Heave a-
way, heave a-way, They comb their hair with
cod-fish bones, We are bound for Aus-tra-lia!

Chorus
Heave a-way, ye bul-ly, bul-ly boys, Heave a-
way, heave a-way, Heave a-way and
don't ye make a noise, We are bound for Aus-tra-lia.

2. Cape Cod boys, they have no sleds, heave away, heave away,
   They slide downhill on codfish heads, we are bound for Australia.
      Chorus

3. Cape Cod men, they have no sails, heave away, heave away,
   They sail their boats with codfish tails, we are bound for Australia.
      Chorus

4. Cape Cod wives, they have no pins, heave away, heave away,
   They pin their gowns with codfish fins, we are bound for Australia.
      Chorus

The Black Ball Line were ships that carried mail and freight between Liverpool and New York beginning in 1818. Each ship carried a crimson swallow-tail flag with a black ball in the center.

BLOW THE MAN DOWN

Sea Chantey

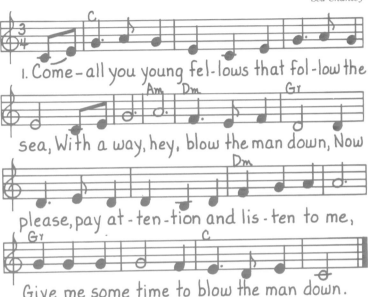

1. Come-all you young fel-lows that fol-low the sea, With a way, hey, blow the man down, Now please, pay at-ten-tion and lis-ten to me, Give me some time to blow the man down.

2. There are tinkers and tailors, shoemakers and all,
   With a way, hey, blow the man down,
   They're all shipped for sailors on board the Black Ball,
   Give me some time to blow the man down.
3. 'Tis when the Black Baller is clear of the land,
   With a way, hey, blow the man down,
   The crew musters aft at the word of command,
   Give me some time to blow the man down.
4. Pay attention to orders, now you, one and all,
   With a way, hey, blow the man down,
   For see, right above you there flies the Black Ball,
   Give me some time to blow the man down.

The Erie Canal, completed in 1825 between Buffalo and Albany, New York, joined the Great Lakes System with the Atlantic Ocean. Boats were pulled by mules which walked alongside the canal on towpaths. The muledrivers were called towpath boys or "hoggies."

ERIE CANAL

Canal Work Song

1. I've got a mule, her name is Sal, Fif-teen

miles on the E-rie Ca-nal. She's a good old

work-er and a good old pal. Fif-teen

miles on the E-rie Ca-nal. We've hauled some

bar-ges in our day, Filled with lum-ber,

coal and hay, And we know ev-'ry inch of the

28

way, From Al-ba-ny to— Buf—fa-lo.—

Chorus

Low bridge, ev'-ry-bod-y down, Low bridge, for we're

com-in' to a town; And you'll al-ways know your

neigh-bor, You'll al-ways know your pal, If you've

ev-er nav-i-gat-ed on the E-rie Ca-nal.

2. Git up there, Sal, we passed that lock,
   Fifteen miles on the Erie Canal,
And we'll make Rome 'fore six o'clock,
   Fifteen miles on the Erie Canal.
Just one more trip and back we'll go
   Through the rain and sleet and snow,
'Cause we know ev'ry inch of the way
   From Albany to Buffalo.
      Chorus

DOWN THE RIVER

River Chantey

1. The riv-er is up and the chan-nel is deep,
The wind is stead-y and strong,— Oh, won't we
have a jol-ly good time As we go sail-ing a-long.

Chorus

Down the riv-er, oh, down the riv-er, Oh,
down the riv-er we go,—— Down the riv-er, oh,
down the riv-er, Oh, down the O-hi-o.——

2. The river is up and the channel is deep, the wind is steady and strong,
Oh, Dinah, put the hoecake on, as we go sailing along.
    Chorus

3. The river is up and the channel is deep, the wind is steady and strong,
The waves do splash from shore to shore, as we go sailing along.
    Chorus